3

Stepping Up In Reading
Building Accuracy and Fluency

D1216798

Phyllis Bertin
Eileen Perlman

EDUCATORS PUBLISHING SERVICE
Cambridge and Toronto

Illustrator: Elizabeth McGoldrick
Typesetting: Rebecca C. Royen
Managing Editor: Sheila Neylon

Educators Publishing Service
800.225.5750
www.epsbooks.com

Printed in U.S.A.
ISBN 0-8388-5141-X

2 3 4 5 6 VHG 08 07 06 05 04

Stepping Up In Reading
Building Accuracy and Fluency

Stepping Up In Reading is based on research from the National Institute of Child Health and Human Development,[1] which reaffirms the impact of accuracy and fluency on reading comprehension. These workbooks contain word, phrase, and sentence lists that provide practice in decoding, word recognition, and expressive reading. The lists have been phonetically controlled and follow the sequence in the *Preventing Academic Failure* (PAF)[2] reading program. *Stepping Up In Reading* can be used as a supplement to any reading program for beginning or remedial readers or as a component of PAF.

The goal is for students to read text so that it sounds like spoken language. The more oral reading sounds like speech, the better the understanding of text. Therefore, each list should be read and re-read with a teacher until students are reading the word lists automatically and reading the phrase and sentence lists with proper expression. The lists are meant to be read under the direction of an adult who can provide appropriate guidance. Teachers should focus students on sound/symbol associations and model blending, proper pronunciation, phrasing, and intonation.

Activities such as categorizing, finding synonyms, and interpreting idioms are given for most lists. Their purpose is to develop comprehension by focusing students on text meaning and to ensure that students are not word-calling. These activities require higher levels of cognition than simply decoding words, and they are an important part of a reading curriculum. They should always be done in class with a teacher and used to stimulate group discussions about the meaning of the words and text.

Word Lists[3]

The word lists contain isolated words. Without contextual clues which force the application of decoding skills. The word lists provide not only a vehicle for teaching students how to blend sounds into words but also the practice needed to make the transition from deliberate decoding to recognizing words without conscious effort.

Students should read the columns down rather than across. It is an improper reading strategy to read horizontal text without grouping the words into meaningful units. Each student takes a turn reading a word. If a student does not recognize a word, he decodes it by saying the sound of each phonogram and blending the sounds into words.

---

[1] See the report of the National Reading Panel (May 2000), titled *Teaching Students to Read* (www.nationalreadingpanel.org).

[2] PAF is a multisensory structured language program (Orton-Gillingham-based) for teaching reading, handwriting, and spelling to students in grades K to 3. It is coordinated with the Merrill Reading Program.

[3] The corresponding lesson level in the PAF program is indicated on each list.

Blending sounds into words can be a slow, sound-by-sound process that the teacher will have to model when students are first learning to read; however, with sufficient practice the blending will become rapid and automatic. Gradually, after much daily practice, students will move from letter-to-letter decoding to the syllable-by-syllable reading needed for longer words and whole-word recognition.

The goal is for each word to be read as it would be naturally spoken. The correct pronunciation is necessary to get to the word meaning. The teacher, or students, can supply the meaning of unfamiliar words, but do not try to turn the word lists into vocabulary lessons. Students find it very difficult to learn the meaning of new words when they are not in context; it is better to address vocabulary development when reading text.

Phrase Lists

Poor readers are often dysfluent, reading word-by-word instead of processing print into meaningful units. The main purpose of reading phrase lists is to provide practice in reading *chunks* of language. Phrase lists also provide students with examples of proper word usage and can be used for sentence construction activities. Not all of the word combinations on these lists are phrases by strict definition. (For example, some are subordinate clauses.) For the purposes of this book, we use the term phrase to mean a group of words that is not a complete sentence.

Explain to students that the word combinations on their phrase lists are only parts of sentences and therefore lack punctuation. Tell them that they are reading these phases to practice connecting the words so that their reading sounds the way they speak. As with blending, the teacher must model how the phrases should be read until students start reading more fluently.

Sentence Lists

The main purpose of sentence lists is to provide an opportunity for teaching and practicing reading with proper intonation and pauses (i.e., reading with expression). Reading with expression is facilitated by teaching students to pay attention to typographical signals, such as ending punctuation, commas, and quotation marks. Sentences are numbered so that students do not mistake them as part of a connected text.

Activities

The suggested activities at the bottom of the pages are meant to be done after the lists have been read for decoding and fluency practice. They encourage the re-reading of the lists and improve reading comprehension. These are group activities and should be done under s teacher's guidance.

All the lists should be sent home and read to an adult for extra practice. Starting with *Stepping Up In Reading Book 2*, the activities that involve having children produce oral sentences, can also be assigned as independent work or homework by having children write three to five original sentences.

For a full description of the PAF program, visit www.pafprogram.com.

right	slight	highway
tight	tightest	tonight
night	mighty	flashlight
light	lighter	spotlight
high	highest	midnight
might	fighter	upright
fight	sighed	lightning
sigh	brightest	insight
sight	slightly	daylight
bright	sightless	delight
thigh	sunlight	firefighter
flight	nightmare	delightful

Circle things that can be frightening.

the brightest star in the sky	a flight of stairs
a delayed flight	the brave firefighters
right or left	their high school
might or might not	right-handed
as dark as night	too tight
a slight grin	the dim lights
a bolt of lightning	rocket flight
night school	right away
three-way light bulbs	as bright as the sun
thunder and lightning	the high jump
later tonight	an amazing nightmare
high tide	the flight recorder
in the spotlight	after midnight
the fighter pilot	a delightful party
day and night	all right
like a mighty beast	a tight fit
fifty lightning bugs	really bright
a thigh bone	on the highway
civil rights	the lady's flashlight

2   Underline the three similes, and use each one in a sentence.

harden	beaten	frightened
sharpen	shorten	tightened
darken	sweeten	shortening
frighten	broken	sweetener
eaten	blacken	sharpened
fallen	lighten	shortened
taken	chosen	darkened
brighten	awaken	sweetened
deepen	sunken	awakened
frozen	spoken	brightened
thicken	sicken	hardened
tighten	sharpener	frightening

---

tightened her grip

shortened his pants

sharpened the crayons

thickened the gravy

awakened at midnight

sweetened the tea

brightened my day

hardened the clay

darkened the sky

frightened by lightning

Use each of the first five phrases in a sentence that has the word *because*.

open	kitten	maiden
even	garden	evenly
seven	siren	gardener
mitten	linen	suddenly
kitchen	happen	happening
chicken	raven	happened
sudden	pollen	seventeen

---

the fire siren	even numbers
seventeen minus nine	a litter of kittens
the kitchen sink	chicken pox
a sudden chill	happened quickly
linen napkins	the can opener
her maiden name	my kindergarten teacher
even-tempered	the seven seas
all of a sudden	seventeen lightning bugs

Circle the words and phrases that name people or animals that can breathe.

 **woman**

 **women**

1. That woman is the tallest player on the basketball team.

2. The women on the basketball team are all amazing athletes.

3. A woman is an adult female human being.

4. The women stared in amazement as the lightning struck the oak tree.

5. Suddenly the woman awoke from a nightmare.

6. Women in the United States did not have the right to vote until 1920.

7. Seventeen women and seven men teach math at my sister's high school.

8. The woman who lives next to us happens to have seven kittens!

9. What is that woman's maiden name?

10. The women who live upstairs play in a band.

Underline and re-read the sentences that are about more than one female.

target	pocket	socket
basket	velvet	packet
rocket	carpet	banquet
magnet	ticket	bracket
market	comet	cricket
jacket	trumpet	helmet
planet	closet	supermarket
bucket	blanket	wastebasket
racket	bonnet	pocketful

---

the planet Mars	pocket-size
carpet sweeper	bike helmet
rocket ship	chicken cutlet
ticket taker	tennis racket
wedding banquet	bucket seat
winter jacket	a woven basket
linen closet	baby blanket
light socket	flea market
blanket chest	bar magnet

6   Circle the words and phrases that name containers.

insulted	preventing	pretended
punished	container	published
frightening	awakened	tightened
silently	injected	connecting
opened	expected	sharpener
frequently	suspenders	insisted
conducted	evenly	predicting
shortening	sweetener	darkened
publisher	invented	disrupting
happened	opening	protected
consented	finished	consulted
politely	visited	banished
delightful	protecting	slivered
cleverest	insightful	departed
retainer	vanished	eventful
brightened	suddenly	carpeting

In the first column, circle an antonym for the word *rarely*.
In the second column, circle an antonym for the word *appeared*.
In the third column, circle an antonym for the word *arrived*.

Am I adding a vowel suffix?
Does the root word end with one consonant?
Put your pencil on the first vowel and count.

1, 2 – Doubling I do!

Root Word	Suffix	New Word
drop	-ing	
step	-ed	
fast	-est	
red	-ness	
snap	-y	
clean	-er	
glad	-ly	
skip	-ed	
rub	-ing	
star	-y	
tight	-en	
trim	-ed	
quick	-ly	
slim	-est	
scrub	-ed	
fun	-y	

Add each suffix to the root word, and then read the new word.

	Root Word	Suffix
running	run	ing
shipped		
starring		
muddy		
biggest		
scrubbed		
flatten		
mopped		
redder		
choppy		
stepping		
slimmer		
scrubbing		
trimmed		
funny		
fatten		
foggy		
dropper		

For each word, write the root word and suffix in the correct columns.

9

happen	seven	garden
happens	sevens	gardens
happened	seventy	gardening
happening	seventeen	gardener
thick	fright	short
thickest	frighten	shorter
thicker	frightful	shortly
thicken	frightened	shorten
thickened	frightening	shortening
night	high	bright
nightly	highest	brightest
tonight	highly	brighter
midnight	higher	brighten
nightmare	highway	brightly
sweet	light	sharp
sweetest	lightest	sharper
sweeter	lighter	sharpest
sweeten	lightly	sharpen
sweetening	lighten	sharpens
sweetener	lightning	sharpener
sweetened	delight	sharpened
sweetness	delightful	sharpening

more	score	swore	explore
wore	store	boring	explorer
sore	shore	stored	exploring
core	snore	snoring	drugstore
bore	chore	before	forecast

1. Before you shut off the computer, don't forget to save the letter on my floppy disk.

2. We will read more of Stone Fox today so we can finish it before the end of the week.

3. I have to finish my chores before I can play basketball with you.

4. Would you be frightened to explore the caves along the shore?

5. Would you please store these cartons in your basement?

6. My husband's constant snoring drives me crazy.

7. Not only does that woman have a sore throat, she is running a fever.

8. Please don't ignore me when I am speaking to you!

9. Which is more, two feet or one yard?

10. Long speeches can be so boring.

Discuss the literal and figurative meanings of the idioms in sentences 6 and 7.

Am I adding a vowel suffix?
Does the root word end with one consonant?
Put your pencil on the first vowel and count.

1, 2—Doubling I do!

Root Word	Suffix	Silent *e* Rule?	Doubling Rule?	New Word
shop	-ed		✔	shopped
awake	-en			
sun	-y			
clap	-ed			
fun	-y			
sore	-ly			
scar	-ed			
amaze	-ment			
snore	-ing			
fog	-y			
hug	-ed			
bright	-est			
nose	-y			
use	-ful			
mud	-y			

Decide whether to apply the silent *e* or doubling rule to add each suffix, and then check the appropriate box.
Add each suffix to the root word, and read the new word.

12

bigger	dropped	stepping
flatten	chopper	runner
quitting	redder	muddy
trimmed	skipping	jogged
madder	scarred	budding
dipped	grabbed	starry
foggy	scrubbed	hugged
shipped	sunny	sagging
hummed	snapped	fattest
slimmer	chipped	mopping
rubbed	shopping	clipped
funny	drummer	hopping
floppy	swimmer	thinner
splitting	planned	flipped

Circle the words that describe day or night.

ace	ice
face	nice
race	rice
pace	mice
lace	price
place	slice
space	spice
grace	splice
trace	advice

city	cement	princess
cent	cider	accent
spruce	sincere	accept
truce	excite	priceless
cents	decide	graceful
icy	except	fireplace
spicy	success	someplace
pencil	license	excitement
center	cancel	successful
fancy	stencil	sincerely

14   Circle the adjectives that can describe a person.

paper and pencils

seventeen cents

an ice bucket

a spruce tree

face-to-face

a fairy princess

in the center of the city

a spicy dish

the cement mixer

paced back and forth

my driver's license

a priceless jade ring

decided quickly

an icy highway

skating on thin ice

to say grace

city hall

as cold as ice

a race horse

bad advice

space travel

an ice cream soda

race horses

the price tag

paper place mats

ice skates

hot cider

sincerely yours

tracing the stencils

iced tea

chicken and rice

accepted the gifts

to make a face

a fancy lace jacket

more successful

a nice, cheesy slice of pizza

Underline and re-read the phrases that name things you can eat or drink.

dance	fleece	convince
fence	France	pranced
since	Greece	dancer
chance	distance	glanced
prince	entrance	peaceful
peace	silence	winced
force	clearance	prancing
prance	balance	minced
wince	sentence	dancing
trance	sequence	forceful
glance	lettuce	balancing
mince	practice	practicing

In the first column, circle the synonym for the word *look*.

In the second column, circle the synonym for the word *order*.

16   In the third column, circle the synonym for the word *chopped*.

a peaceful sleep	traveled to Greece
glanced up	since last Sunday
in a trance	a graceful dancer
ice dancing	a peaceful evening
practiced the trumpet	at a glance
a white picket fence	trimmed the sheep's fleece
her last chance	a balance beam
a fleece jacket	in the distance
visited France	a clearance sale
basketball practice	long distance running
the minced garlic	a run-on sentence
space flight	tap dancing
prancing horses	the front entrance
the prince and princess	her bank balance

Underline and re-read the phrases that name physical activities.

1. Once upon a time there lived a prince who was very lonely.

2. We feed our pet mice once a day.

3. Women once wore long dresses and fancy bonnets.

4. I once had a nightmare in which I was lost in space.

5. Once there were homes with no TVs!

6. Computers are much cheaper than they once were.

7. Once and for all, I am not driving in this ice storm!

8. We must leave for basketball practice at once, or we will be late.

9. Once, my computer crashed just as I finished a long report for school.

10. I couldn't understand what you were saying because everyone was talking at once.

11. Once I stopped jogging before school each day, my feet felt fine!

12. Just this once, may I have an ice cream cone before dinner?

13. Once you decide what you want for dinner, I will go shopping at the supermarket.

14. Lightning once struck a spruce tree in the center of the park and split it in two!

15. Once you have sharpened all the pencils, would you please give one to each student?

18   Underline and re-read the sentences in which *once* means what happened in the past.

Am I adding a vowel suffix?
Does the root word end with a consonant?
Put your pencil on the first vowel and count.

1, 2 – Doubling I do!

Root Word	Suffix	Silent *e* Rule?	Doubling Rule?	New Word
thin	-er		✔	thinner
peace	-ful			
fog	-y			
red	-en			
dance	-er			
ice	-y			
plan	-er			
spot	-ed			
slice	-ed			
fat	-est			
race	-ing			
nice	-ly			
swim	-er			
spice	-y			
sun	-y			

Decide whether to apply the silent *e* or doubling rule to add each suffix, and then check the appropriate box.
Add each suffix to the root word, and read the new word.

VCCCV

children	approach	hungry
sandwich	actress	increase
monster	pantry	subtract
empty	explain	inflate
lobster	enclose	angry
complete	inspect	display
Pilgrims	panther	athlete
hundred	concrete	tantrum
extra	exclude	sprinkler
pumpkin	entry	ostrich
explode	instruct	instant
express	partner	hamster
include	complain	inspire
conclude	extreme	address

In the first column, circle the antonym for *full*.

In the second column, circle the antonym for *exit*.

In the third column, circle the antonym for *add*.

subtracted	completely	exploded
complained	concluding	displayed
enchanted	enclosed	including
instantly	instructed	extremely
impressed	inflated	increasing

---

the kitchen pantry	kindergarten children
a lobster trap	completely finished
throw a tantrum	a dance partner
a store display	tired and hungry
the frozen tundra	concluding remarks
extremely angry	one hundred pumpkins
an enchanted kingdom	express mail
the express bus	a pet hamster
name and address	my grandchildren
empty-handed	e-mail address
instant oatmeal	peanut butter and jelly sandwich

In each column, underline and re-read the phrase that describes how someone might feel.

1. The show was so funny that my grandchildren couldn't stop laughing.

2. The women laughed at the sight of the basketball star trying to fit into the tiny chair.

3. Suddenly, the children started laughing at the women in the silly party hats.

4. The children laughed and clapped when their teacher said that they would be going to the circus.

5. My friends laugh at all of my jokes, even when they are not very funny.

6. The woman laughed to herself softly.

7. When you are feeling low, try to laugh away your problems.

8. They might not feel like laughing when their mom gets home and sees the mess they made.

9. Did you hear the ravens laughing and chattering in the trees last night?

10. We could hear the children's laughter as they were ice-skating on the pond.

In the first four sentences, underline the words that tell why someone is laughing.

table	mumble	tremble
pebble	dribble	stumble
tumble	noble	tablecloth
bubble	marble	bumblebee
able	wobble	bubblegum
thimble	stable	grumbled
bible	jumble	crumbling
fumble	nimble	scribbled
nibble	grumble	stumbled
stubble	fable	dribbling
humble	crumble	fumbled
gobble	scribble	trembling

---

to scribble carelessly

a bubble bath

to nibble on crackers

dribbles the basketball

fit and able

gobbling up their lunch

a marble table

a jumble of letters

fumbled the ball

under the table

a horse stable

table manners

trembled with fright

the fable's theme

Circle the words that name something you can hold in your hand.

ruffle	gargle	uncle
giggle	ankle	angle
tickle	rifle	shuffle
sniffle	sprinkle	tingle
bugle	dangle	struggle
buckle	single	chuckle
jingle	pickle	sparkle
tackle	twinkle	tackled
jungle	muffle	goggles
freckle	crackle	muffler
wiggle	tangle	sprinkler

---

a gaggle of geese	stifling heat
a fancy ankle bracelet	a silver belt buckle
crying and sniffling	to tickle your funny bone
dangling earrings	to shuffle the playing cards
to crinkle your nose	a ticklish baby
a crackling fire	to tackle the problem
a sprained ankle	bangles and beads
jingle bells	in a pickle

24   Underline and re-read the phrases that name things that would make good gifts.

1. To inflate something means to fill it with gas or air and make it expand.

2. If you inflate that tire too much, it may explode!

3. A person who is very skilled in sports is called an athlete.

4. The road inclines so steeply that the children can't bike safely on it.

5. Since we are late, let's take the express bus right to the center of the city.

6. We once read a scary story about a princess who lived in an enchanted kingdom.

7. Concrete becomes very hard when it is dry.

8. Please write your name and address on the bottom of your paper.

9. To instruct someone means to teach them.

10. Please include an extra sandwich in my lunchbox because I get extremely hungry.

11. When someone tickles your funny bone, it means that they make you laugh.

12. The store display included fancy bracelets and dangling earrings.

13. Sometimes when my baby sister is tired or hungry, she may throw a tantrum.

14. Can you subtract seventeen from twenty?

Underline and re-read the sentences that are definitions.

riddle	sample	brittle
apple	cattle	tattle
maple	staple	bridle
little	pimple	topple
puddle	drizzle	kettle
bottle	simple	crumble
middle	huddle	cuddle
title	needle	littlest
handle	sizzle	cuddly
saddle	battle	puzzled
bundle	dimple	stapler
paddle	settle	handlebars
cradle	ladle	candlestick
beetle	fiddle	bottleneck
startle	ripple	rattlesnake
puzzle	shuttle	battleship
candle	trample	settlement

Circle the words that name useful household items.

middle school	jokes and riddles
as cuddly as a baby	cattle ranch
stampeding cattle	a needle in a haystack
a right angle	to blow out the candles
the space shuttle	rocking the cradle
maple trees	bottle opener
apple cider	a bundle of sticks
the chapter title	baked apples
a plastic bottle	fiddling with his pencil
in the middle of the road	a simple math problem
a puzzling problem	brittle bones
kindling a fire	on pins and needles
the sizzling bacon	to solve a riddle
topple over	a set of kettledrums
dimpled cheeks	a pair of candlesticks

Underline and re-read the phrases that name things that can make you think.

people

1. People who try hard to tackle their problems can become extremely successful.

2. The people giggled at his silly riddles.

3. A line of people waited all night to get tickets for the rock concert.

4. The mall was full of people shopping for gifts.

5. They closed the middle school today so that people could vote.

6. People who want to do well in school study hard.

7. People should be kind to one another.

8. It isn't easy for tall people to fit into compact cars.

9. A king's duty to his people includes being fair and wise.

10. Some people like to baby-sit for their grandchildren on the weekends.

11. The people cheered when the center sank a basket.

12. All people who have the right to vote should cast their ballots.

cell	spice	candle
coach	care	coffee
call	since	cement
nice	cancel	except
place	city	candy
dance	accept	practice
face	advice	citrus
coast	comet	cattle
ice	cable	carpet
cent	cactus	sincere
space	center	collect
rice	excite	pencil
coat	fancy	decide
peace	census	success

In the first column, circle the synonym for *penny*.
In the second column, circle the synonym for *middle*.
In the third column, circle the synonym for *gather*.

age	gorge	margin
page	fringe	legend
large	bulge	stingy
cage	singe	digest
gem	hinge	stranger
huge	charge	teenager
rage	strange	gentleman
wage	plunge	gentlemen
stage	gentle	stagecoach
barge	magic	gingersnaps
range	ginger	congested

---

magic tricks	ginger ale
to make change	stage fright
a strange story	Ice Age
a gentle breeze	a huge puddle
page numbers	a large rattlesnake
to plunge into	a fringed lampshade
the title page	the sports pages
to behave strangely	the right margin
a Web page	changed seats

Underline and re-read the phrases that describe parts of a book.

1. Last week I just had the sniffles, but today my lungs are all congested.

2. Try to keep your place on the page while we are reading these legends and fables.

3. I've never been in a play because I get stage fright.

4. Print the numbers from one to ten in the margin of your paper, please.

5. The gentleman rose and gave the old lady his seat on the bus.

6. The cradle was swaying gently back and forth in the breeze.

7. I laughed so hard during dinner that I couldn't digest the meal!

8. A gentle breeze rustled the leaves of the maple trees.

9. To singe something means to burn it lightly.

10. At what age do people get a driver's license?

11. The hamsters that are sleeping in that large cage are extremely gentle.

12. Are the gems in her wedding band real?

13. Do you like the taste of ginger ale?

14. A gorge is a narrow, steep-walled canyon.

15. Something that is huge is very large

16. A barge is a flat-bottomed boat.

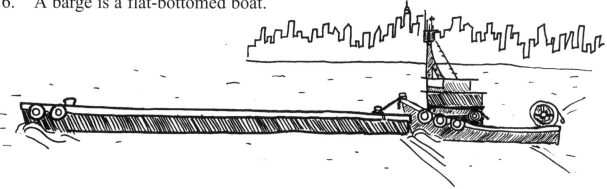

Underline and re-read the sentences that are definitions.

Am I adding a vowel suffix?
Does the root word end with a consonant?
Put your pencil on the first vowel and count.

1, 2—Doubling I do!

Root Word	Suffix	Silent *e* Rule?	Doubling Rule?	New Word
hop	-ing		✓	hopping
hope	-ing			
file	-ed			
fill	-ed			
tap	-ing			
tape	-ing			
hope	-ed			
hop	-ed			
mop	-ing			
mope	-ing			
scare	-ed			
scar	-ed			
stare	-ing			
star	-ing			

Decide whether to apply the silent *e* or doubling rule to add each suffix, and then check the appropriate box.
Add each suffix to the root word, and read the new word.

judge	fudge	dredge
dodge	ledge	badger
badge	nudge	midget
bridge	wedge	gadget
lodge	hedge	budget
budge	smudge	fidget
pledge	trudge	hedgehog

---

to trim the hedges	a gray badger
a star-shaped badge	a huge sledgehammer
to cross the bridge	dodge ball
a large, black smudge	the railroad bridge
dodging the traffic	the edge of the cliff
to plan a budget	fudge cake
a rustic lodge	to settle a grudge
to dredge the river	the bridge of your nose
the judge's gavel	a pledge of friendship
to play bridge	a midget racing car

Underline and re-read all the phrases with the word *bridge*, and discuss the word's multiple meanings.

1. Some eagles build huge nests in trees near rivers.

2. My uncle likes to build model airplanes as a hobby.

3. We need to build a fire for our campsite before night falls.

4. I have decided that someday I would like to be able to build bridges.

5. Exercise helps people build strong bones.

6. Some people can build their own Web sites.

7. The hunters used large stones to build a lodge on the edge of the lake.

8. Some beavers built a little dam in the middle of our pond.

9. The Pilgrims built a settlement on Cape Cod Bay in 1620.

10. The city built a wide road from the airport to the hotels.

11. The excitement built because the baseball game was in the last inning.

12. Our kitchen has built-in maple cabinets under the sink.

13. What kind of building is a lodge?

14. The people who live in our apartment building are very friendly.

15. The Empire State Building, which was built in Manhattan in 1930, is 1,453 feet high!

Underline the word or phrase in each of the first ten sentences that names something that can be built.

mopping	striped
moping	stripped
bitter	slimmer
biter	slimmest
biting	slimy
robber	gripped
robed	griped
robbed	griping
robbing	gripping
hopped	taped
hoped	tapped
hopping	taping
hoping	tapping
cute	scaring
cuter	scarring
cutter	scary
cutest	scared
cutting	scarred
stared	filled
starred	filed
starring	filing
staring	filling
starry	filler

cabbage	cottage	rummage
luggage	damage	shortage
bandage	package	salvage
message	savage	damaged
garbage	passage	passageway
village	storage	manager
manage	baggage	management

---

all the baggage

the skunk cabbage

built a cottage

to build a village

savage beasts

a shortage of bandages

the manager of the supermarket

approached the passageway

an e-mail message

the baggage car

the fire damage

a rummage sale

a storage building

an express package

cottage cheese

in storage

the spitting image of his dad

a package of sunflower seeds

the smell of the garbage cans

managed to change the light bulb

Circle the words that name things you might take on a trip.

age	geese	digest
gap	large	gusty
stage	legends	gentle
strange	gallon	ginger
huge	stingy	baggage
gears	bigger	foggy
page	magic	agent
gems	margin	giving
gills	gadget	garbage
change	tragic	budget

---

gear shift	giving me change
a huge gap	strange gadgets
bigger margins	a large stage
magic show	gentle geese
gallons of ginger ale	a stingy gentleman
gusty winds	a real gem
a tragic legend	a real estate agent

Circle the words that can describe a person.

child	find	rind	blinds
mild	wind	hind	behind
wild	mind	grind	kindest
kind	bind	blind	childish

---

to bind up her hair	an act of kindness
a mild winter	lemon rind
a kindly gentleman	to grind one's teeth
hind legs	finders keepers
mild summer breezes	to make up your mind
all my children	falling behind
blinded by the bright lights	to change one's mind
behind the garbage can	to wind the clock
grinding the chestnuts	childish games
a kind of wild dog	to close the blinds

Underline and re-read the phrases that describe things you can do with your hands.

-old	-ost	-olt
old	most	colt
told	post	bolt
cold	host	jolt
gold	hostess	molt
hold	mostly	bolted
fold	postage	molten
bold	postcard	molting
sold	postpone	jolted
mold	hosted	thunderbolt
scold	uppermost	
moldy		
olden		
golden		
scolded		
coldest		
blindfold		

bolted upright in bed

postage stamps

folded her hands

a smoldering fire

bolted the lock

to hold hands

holds his temper

to grow old

the bold settlers

has cold feet

twelve years old

to hold a grudge

cold storage

an old friend

both of my children

a bold plan

the goldfish bowl

moldy cheese

old age

both gold and silver

cold and wet

scolded the dog

a bolt of lightning

to catch a cold

a gold mine

molten lava

a kind hostess

a frightening thunderbolt

Underline and re-read the phrases that name things that are hot.

her	person	adverb
germ	perfume	hermit
nerve	perhaps	termite
serve	perfect	perspire
verb	gerbil	preserve
clerk	mermaid	concern
stern	deserve	iceberg
swerve	concert	serpent
sherbet	desert	permit
expert	lantern	pattern

---

jack-o'-lantern

a supermarket clerk

a perfect score

a hermit crab

a rock concert

sea serpent

deserves a treat

a computer expert

a wild life preserve

a building permit

her pet gerbil

a perfect gentleman

a stern person

swerved the car

perfume bottles

lemon sherbet

the tip of the iceberg

to get on someone's nerves

Underline and re-read the phrases that name things that have legs.

1. Are there any e-mail messages for me?

2. Try not to damage any of those perfume bottles on the dressing table.

3. Do we have any extra milk to make fudge tonight?

4. Perhaps you do not feel any better because you haven't been resting.

5. Is anybody home?

6. My uncle lives in Vermont, and he wouldn't want to live anywhere else.

7. I don't want to talk to anyone until I finish reading this chapter.

8. The left end made a hard tackle, but the running back managed to score anyway.

9. Come over anytime you feel like it, and we'll practice for the concert.

10. Is there anything left to eat in the picnic basket?

11. Before I can drive you anywhere, I have to finish addressing these packages.

12. After they retire, many people decide to go back to school.

13. There are many kinds of sherbet, but I like lemon the best.

14. Many of my friends attended the rock concert last Friday night.

15. Many old villages are built on the edge of rivers

write	wring	wriggle
wrote	wrung	wrapper
wrist	wren	written
wrap	wreath	wreckage
wreck	wrench	wristband
wrong	wrinkle	shipwreck

1. Please wrap the baby in a blanket, and put her in the cradle.

2. Be sure to throw away any candy wrappers in the garbage.

3. The rain wrecked any plans we had to go on a picnic today.

4. Your wrist connects your hand to your arm.

5. We practice our handwriting every day in school.

6. Wrap the bandage tightly so no germs get inside!

7. There are many shipwrecks at the bottom of the sea.

8. It is polite to send a written thank-you note when you get a gift.

9. The child couldn't hold onto the huge fish because it kept wriggling in her hands.

10. I can't finish writing the speech because something is wrong with my computer.

11. I think that gentleman got up on the wrong side of the bed today!

12. Two wrongs don't make a right.

Discuss the meaning of the idiom in sentence 11 and the proverb in sentence 12.   43

age	post	fold
ages	posted	folded
aging	poster	folder
ageless	postage	unfold
teenage	postcard	blindfold
complete	manage	command
completing	managed	commanding
completes	managing	commanded
completed	manager	commander
completely	management	commandment
kind	large	bubble
kinder	larger	bubbles
kindly	largest	bubbling
kindest	enlarge	bubbled
kindness	enlarging	bubbly
mankind	enlargement	bubblegum
place	gentle	anyone
placed	gentlest	anybody
places	gentler	anytime
placing	gently	anyplace
placement	gentleman	anything
misplace	gentlemen	anywhere

fantastic	introduce	October
remember	acrobat	Alaska
cucumber	decorate	September
excellent	customer	Canada
valentine	elastic	Alabama
umbrella	celebrate	Thanksgiving
seventy	expensive	Internet
eleven	advertise	Kentucky
ivory	assembly	Halloween
monument	cabinet	December
gigantic	beverage	Columbus
important	detective	Montana
adjective	utensil	November
exercise	recognize	Wisconsin
tornado	grocery	Atlantic

Explain why each of the words in the third column is capitalized.
Circle the states.

eighty passengers	performed yesterday
cucumber salad	to celebrate the holidays
a perfect performance	expensive to advertise
interesting patterns	helped a customer
seven continents	had an emergency
a gigantic crocodile	ice cold beverages
kindergarten classes	many different examples
a fantastic concert	wrote and illustrated
spicy seasonings	introduced my neighbor
an important message	made quite a difference
built-in cabinets	exercises with weights
a holiday assembly	difficult to solve
electric lights	carpenter's hammer
kitchen utensils	one hundred percent attendance
an excellent reference	grocery store
ivory bracelet and earrings	recognized the handwriting

In the first column, underline the adjective in each phrase.

weigh	eight	eighth	freight
weight	eighty	eighteen	sleigh

neighbor

---

gorilla	different	difference
balcony	Idaho	illustrate
allowance	difficult	reference
rectangle	crocodile	chimpanzee
messenger	romantic	advantage
seasoning	electric	concentrate
operate	permanent	Minnesota
porcupine	yesterday	kindergarten
continent	carpenter	independent
vaccinate	octopus	orangutan
Tennessee	appendix	interesting
salamander	Nevada	emergency
conference	performance	independence
attendance	ambulance	interference
satellite	holiday	passenger

Circle the mammals.

fur	purse	turban
hurt	Thursday	Saturn
hurl	turtle	cursive
curb	purple	hurdle
burn	disturb	overturn
blur	further	sturdy
turn	turnip	turtleneck
urge	urgent	turnpike
burnt	survive	Saturday
nurse	burlap	nursery
church	surprise	hamburger
burst	furnish	turpentine

In the first column, circle a synonym for *rotate*.

In the second column, circle a synonym for *important*.

48   In the third column, circle a synonym for *strong*.

energy	family	citizen
athletic	uniform	substitute
innocent	centimeter	Mexico
committee	centipede	evidence
allergic	Africa	illustrated
educate	maximum	remembering
interrupt	minimum	decorated
deposit	difficult	educated
recommend	president	exercising
average	Jupiter	permanently
coconut	sensitive	concentrating
Delaware	Pacific	recommended
accident	estimate	interrupted
confidence	candidate	imitating

Circle one state, one country, one continent, and one ocean.

know	knife	known	knuckle
knee	knives	kneel	knick-knack
knot	knob	knelt	kneecap
knit	knock	knight	knapsack

---

full of knots

a knuckle ball

to kneel in the sand

knee socks

knitted scarves

forks and knives

a know-it-all

cabinet knobs

a well-known candidate

Thursday night

cursive writing

hamburger buns

curly hair

nursery school

church steeple

a surprise party

to burst out laughing

to turn off the lights

the school nurse

burnt toast

a right turn

next Saturday

furry mittens

to turn off

the furthest planet

an urgent message

eighteen burlap sacks

to take a turn

bursting with pride

surfing the Internet

Underline and re-read the phrases that name things commonly found in a kitchen.

1. In the Middle Ages, many knights served the king.

2. The running back injured his kneecap when he was tackled yesterday.

3. Most people know that Thanksgiving is the fourth Thursday in November.

4. The batter knocked the knuckle ball over the fence in the eighth inning.

5. Last Saturday we painted the knobs on the kitchen cabinets bright yellow!

6. Before we go on the hike, we have to be sure both knapsacks are packed.

7. Please knock before you enter, and do not disturb me while I am writing.

8. Did you know that Saturn is the second largest planet?

9. The school nurse is knitting a purple blanket for her baby.

10. I know my uncle's feelings will be hurt if we don't invite him to the surprise party.

11. There are many different kinds of knots.

12. I have never known a person with such a knack for getting along with people.

13. Someone who thinks he knows everything is called a know-it-all.

14. We knelt in the sand near the surf to see if any of the baby turtles were surviving.

15. Your knee connects your thigh to your lower leg, and your knuckle connects your finger to your hand.

In the first seven sentences, underline the phrases that tell *when*.

sir	skirt	thirst
girl	firm	thirsty
bird	shirt	circus
gird	chirp	dirty
dirt	birch	thirty
stir	swirl	thirteen
birth	whirl	birthday
first	smirk	confirm
third	flirt	circulate
shirt	squirt	hummingbird

---

thirty-eight	a flock of birds
shirt sleeves	thirteen years old
the third grade	the first lady
chirping birds	a traffic circle
dear sir	first class
eighty-first	a surprise birthday party
a clump of dirt	a three-ring circus
eats like a bird	hungry and thirsty

Underline and re-read all the phrases that contain number words.

a cold beverage

a circus acrobat

Independence Day

grocery store

seventy-eight

deposit slip

vice-president

his weekly allowance

a difficult exam

gorillas and chimpanzees

family gathering

a romantic valentine

electric fans

United States

Halloween costume

ivory tusks

school assembly

porcupine quills

the broken umbrella

Columbus Day

emergency exit

to take the attendance

an electric eel

the rings of Jupiter

batting average

North Dakota

to make a difference

an athletic uniform

a difficult math problem

tea kettle

traffic accident

eleven centimeters

Thanksgiving dinner

an independent thinker

the kitchen cabinets

St. Valentine's Day

a substitute teacher

volcanic ash

Underline and re-read the phrases that name or mention a holiday.

out	ground	around
loud	ounce	pronoun
ouch	blouse	thousand
noun	bounce	account
foul	pouch	announce
found	hound	discount
house	snout	flounder
sound	crouch	pronounce
south	mount	dugout
proud	pounce	outfit
mouse	grouch	without
shout	grout	outside
count	trout	blackout
flour	our	lighthouse
pound	sour	playground
couch	mouth	farmhouse
spout	scour	underground
mound	about	loudspeaker
scout	aloud	outstanding

54   Circle five adjectives, and use them to describe any five nouns.

three thousand, four	
two thousand, one hundred	
six thousand, seven hundred thirty	
eight thousand, two hundred eleven	
twenty-one thousand, five hundred seventeen	
thirty thousand, three hundred	
twelve thousand, eighty-seven	
seventy thousand, six hundred thirteen	
six hundred ninety-nine thousand	
nine hundred eighty thousand, four hundred ten	
one hundred twenty-two thousand, eighty-eight	
seven hundred thousand, two hundred five	

Write each number in numeral form.

now	crown	trowel
how	prowl	download
owl	frown	sunflower
cow	clown	nightgown
down	flower	downtown
bow	brown	somehow
vow	drown	anyhow
crowd	powder	however
wow	towel	downstairs
howl	power	crowded
brow	vowel	brownish
plow	shower	prowler
gown	allow	powerful
growl	drowsy	allowed
town	tower	showering

In the first column, circle a synonym for *promise*.
In the second column, circle a synonym for *permit*.

In the third column, circle a synonym for *but*.

the children's playhouse	Web browser
lost and found	the pollen count
not allowed	the mouth of the river
a crowd of people	a herd of cows
proper nouns	grayish brown
outside the church	to turn out the lights
sour pickles	to find out
apartment house	an elegant gown
up and down	blurts out
out of sight	the golden crown
sweet and sour	as loud as thunder
a mound of dirt	a pack of hounds
outer space	to burst out laughing
a foul ball	thirty thousand
the pitcher's mound	a bank account
a loud pounding sound	a merry-go-round
South Dakota	computer mouse
eight ounces	down in the dumps
vowels and consonants	on cloud nine
downloaded the program	to throw in the towel

Discuss the literal and figurative meanings of the idiom in each of the last three phrases.

1. How many feet are in a yard?	
2. How much is seventy-seven plus eighty-eight?	
3. How many hundreds in one thousand?	
4. How much is one third of fifteen?	
5. How many days are in December?	
6. If you add two odd numbers, will the sum be odd or even?	
7. If you subtract thirty-one from eighty, what is the difference?	
8. How many even numbers are there between one and twenty?	
9. If it takes two hours to walk five miles, how long will it take to walk fifteen miles?	
10. If you practice ice skating one hour every day, how many hours will you practice in a week?	
11. How many dimes would you need to get a bottle of perfume that costs $2.40?	

Answer these math questions.

1. Many people came together for the big parade downtown.

2. My mom and I go to the mall together on rainy days.

3. We can always go together to the playground if you're unsure of the way.

4. After a big storm, my friends and I almost always play together in the snow.

5. Friends should always stick together!

6. We almost have this difficult puzzle of the United States all together.

7. The man ate three hamburgers and two hotdogs altogether!

8. The two women counted their change and found that they had only fifty-five cents altogether.

9. My friend rushed home after school so we could play together.

10. My uncle has six grandchildren altogether.

11. After the baby broke the flower pot, we could not put it back together again.

12. Mix flour, eggs, milk and melted butter together to make pancakes.

In the first four sentences, underline the phrases that tell *where*.

sunlight	loudspeaker	birthday
however	turtleneck	anybody
playground	sunflower	nightgown
flashlight	postcard	anything
everything	rattlesnake	wastebasket
gentleman	timeout	fireplace
anyone	everyone	daylight
anytime	outline	clockwise
downtown	anyway	basketball
goldfish	without	blackbird
peppermint	anyplace	everywhere
downstairs	lighthouse	everybody
spotlight	grandchildren	wristband
highway	firefighter	anywhere
someplace	shipwreck	handlebars
underground	somehow	meanwhile

In the first column, circle the adverb that tells *when*.
In the second column, circle the adverb that tells *where*.
60   In the third column, circle the adverb that tells *how*.

work	worry	needlework
world	worship	worthwhile
word	worsen	workshop
worm	homework	worsening
worth	workman	worldwide
worse	worthy	workbench
worst	working	password
wordy	worthless	workout

---

give one's word	will worry a lot
fine needlework	worse than ever
two hours of homework	on top of the world
digging for worms	computer network
crossword puzzle	a work day
work sheet	worthwhile results
around the world	a word of advice
to eat your words	a can of worms
out of this world	World Wide Web
a house of worship	work of art
word processing	a word to the wise

Underline and re-read the phrases that are about technology.

Why did the farmer name his pig *Ink*?

He named him Ink because he kept running out of his **pen**.

Why did the silly man try to eat the lamp?

He wanted a **light** snack.

How is an old car like a baby?

It always has a **rattle**.

Why did the bee call the flowers lazy?

It called the flowers lazy because they were always in a **bed**.

Why is an empty pocket always the same?

It is always the same because there is no **change** in it.

How do you charge a battery?

You **charge** it with your credit card.

How do you make a slow runner **fast**?

You stop feeding him.

Why did the teacher have sunglasses on?

She had sunglasses on because her students were so **bright**!

Discuss the multiple meanings of the words in bold.

war	warmth	quart
warm	award	quartz
warn	warning	quarter
wharf	wardrobe	quarrel
warp	warden	quartet
ward	reward	headquarters
swarm	quarry	quarterback

---

global warming

a quarter to eleven

a marble quarry

tug-of-war

a quart of milk

a jazz quartet

four quarters

warning lights

swarming bees

a canary's warble

to post a reward

a fishing wharf

warm-up

to ward off danger

a warm welcome

a warning sign

her summer wardrobe

tackled the quarterback

the highest award

war paint

Circle the words and phrases that name things you can earn.

1. Some cities use waterpower to generate electricity.

2. Concrete is made of cement, pebbles, sand, and water.

3. The quarterback was in hot water because he was late for practice.

4. Water is part of every living thing.

5. Water falls from the sky as rain, hail, sleet, and snow.

6. We should try not to pollute our water supply.

7. The best way to get rid of germs is to clean your hands with soap and water.

8. When water becomes very cold, it freezes into a solid called ice.

9. It is important to drink between six to eight glasses of water a day.

10. A lake is a body of water.

11. Swimming and diving are both water sports.

12. The world's largest waterfall is Angel Falls in South America.

Underline and re-read the two sentences that give advice about keeping healthy.

survive	adverb	circus
correct	market	birthday
farther	urban	garlic
perform	export	suburbs
concept	import	percent
farmer	barber	border
further	perhaps	confirm
forest	absorb	pattern
surprise	urgent	discard
perfect	perfume	energy
artist	concern	circulate
thirsty	afford	hamburger
permit	thirty	entertain
inform	corner	carpenter
deserve	observe	important
disturb	harvest	remember
partner	person	exercise

Circle the words that name occupations.

carry	mirror	current
merry	parrot	burrow
sorry	error	sorrow
hurry	borrow	furrow
berry	narrow	curry
marry	errand	marrow
ferry	barrel	surround
sparrow	flurry	borrowed
carrot	scurry	surrender
cherry	terry	surroundings

(tomorrow)

---

merry-go-round	a barrel of fun
current events	carry-on luggage
the parrot's cage	a flurry of wind
curry powder	a sparrow's nest
the rabbit's burrow	blackberry preserves
cherry blossoms	a narrow bridge
mirror image	bone marrow
to run an errand	a terry cloth robe
in a hurry	surrounded by purple flowers

66   Circle two words that mean to move quickly.

1. Castles were large buildings with high walls, often surrounded by moats.

2. A mirror has a polished glass surface that forms images by reflecting light.

3. A Web browser lets a person use a mouse to explore the Internet.

4. The Pilgrims celebrated the first Thanksgiving in 1621.

5. Canada, the United States, and Mexico are neighbors.

6. Porcupines have sharp quills to protect themselves.

7. Martin Luther King Jr. was an important civil rights leader.

8. Rabbits and other animals make burrows in the ground for shelter and warmth.

9. Gorillas, orangutans, and chimpanzees are all apes and have no tails.

10. A square is a kind of rectangle.

11. Jupiter is the largest planet and is the fifth one from the sun.

12. There are sixteen ounces in one pound.

13. If the President cannot serve out his term, the Vice-President becomes our leader.

14. Every citizen in the United States who is at least eighteen years old has the right to vote.

Underline and re-read the sentences that give historical facts.

won	other	stepmother
ton	dozen	stepbrother
son	cover	otherwise
love	mother	undercover
shove	recover	discovery
front	govern	wonderful
dove	wonder	uncovered
glove	nothing	monthly
sponge	comfort	shoveling
month	shovel	covered
oven	brother	grandson
among	smother	comforted
lovely	Monday	motherly
above	company	government
another	discover	grandmother
comforter	uncover	undiscovered

Circle all the words that name kinds of family members.

above and beyond	had a wonderful time
among friends	fits like a glove
cheaper by the dozen	city government
brotherly love	quite a discovery
monthly meetings	nothing to it
front and center	undiscovered talents
one way or another	love at first sight
every month	smother with kisses
as lovely as a rose	all the comforts of home
an undercover cop	to have tons to do
head over heels in love	once every Monday
once a month	to have a sponge bath
front teeth	love letters
to handle with kid gloves	front page story
a dozen pair of gloves	a covered bridge
the month of December	pick and shovel
boxing gloves	sponge cake
to discover the truth	every other year

Underline and re-read the phrases that tell how often an event might happen.

father

1. Did you know that Barry's stepfather writes front page stories for the paper?

2. A grandfather clock is a tall clock that is often taller than a person!

3. My friend's grandfather is an accountant for the state government.

4. Larry told me that his mother and father married twenty years ago.

5. A father figure is a man who gives you help or advice.

6. The President of the United States is a father figure to many people.

7. The teacher gave his student some fatherly advice.

8. The first time my mother saw my father it was love at first sight.

9. Both my father and grandfather come from Mexico.

10. Ben Franklin was one of the founding fathers of the United States.

11. Some people think that I am the image of my father.

12. Your father's mother is your grandmother.

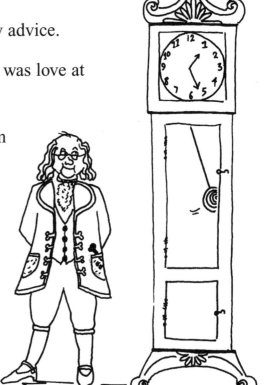

Underline and re-read the sentences that are definitions.

head	headband	deadline
health	heavy	instead
lead	feather	forehead
read	healthy	headlight
thread	pleasant	breathless
spread	ready	breathtaking
bread	ahead	headdress
wealth	already	heavenly
breath	leather	sweatshirt
sweat	meadow	heaviest
deaf	sweater	unhealthy
steady	wealthy	headline
meant	steady	gingerbread

Circle words that name things often made of cloth.

bread and butter	a clean bill of health
already completed	as light as a feather
ahead of	ahead of time
needle and thread	a warm turtleneck sweater
out of breath	ready and able
weather forecast	heavy-duty battery
head over heels in love	pleasant dreams
a cotton-knit sweatshirt	a head of lettuce
heavy-duty equipment	to go ahead
a broken headlight	to spread rapidly
ostrich feathers	to plan ahead
to knead the bread	gingerbread man
ready or not	to take a deep breath
to spread the word	a leather jacket
the head of the class	meet a deadline

Underline and re-read the phrases that name things you might wear to keep warm.

Does the root word end in a *y*?
Is there a consonant before the *y*?
If the answer is yes, **change** the *y* **to** *i* and add the suffix (unless the suffix begins with *i*).

Root Word	Suffix	New Word
try	-ed	
cry	-ing	
study	-ed	
happy	-ly	
baby	-ish	
stay	-ed	
heavy	-ness	
carry	-ing	
marry	-ing	
play	-er	
fly	-ing	
hurry	-ing	
lazy	-est	
cry	-er	
worry	-ed	

Add each suffix to the root word, and read the new word.

	Root Word	**Suffix**
spiciest	spicy	est
grayish		
tried		
emptiness		
hurried		
drowsiness		
copying		
babyish		
heaviest		
carrying		
flier		
married		
laziness		
merrily		
carried		
worrier		
happily		
trying		

Write the root words and the suffixes in the correct columns.

buy

1. If my brother buys a ten-dollar sweatshirt with a twenty-dollar bill, how much change will he get?	
2. If a leather coat costs fifty dollars, how many coats can you buy with two hundred dollars?	
3. My mother wants to buy a loaf of bread. She has two dollars, and the bread costs one dollar and fifty cents. How much change will she get?	
4. If it costs five dollars to buy a dozen muffins, how much will it cost for four dozen?	
5. If my stepbrother buys a computer for one thousand dollars and a printer for two hundred dollars, how much will he pay all together?	
6. To fill his gas can, a truck driver buys two gallons of gas at one dollar and eighty-five cents a gallon. How much does the gas cost him?	
7. My father has five dollars. If he buys a head of lettuce for a dollar and a quarter and a loaf of bread for three dollars and fifty cents, how much money will he have left?	
8. If my mother buys a pair of gloves for twenty-three dollars and my father buys a headlight for eighty-nine dollars, how much will they spend all together?	
9. If I want to buy a quart of milk for one dollar and nine cents, but I only have two quarters, how much more cash do I need?	

Answer the math questions.

great	bear	greatness
steak	wear	underwear
tear	swear	breakable
break	beefsteak	unbreakable
pear	pear-shaped	unbearable

---

a steak knife

a grizzly bear

repair a tear

swearing-in

a great horned owl

breakdown on the highway

great friends of mine

not nice to swear

tears easily

huge bear prints

grin and bear it

to break a leg

great grandfather

as hungry as a bear

lucky break

steak and eggs

a partridge in a pear tree

unbreakable dishes

heavy cotton underwear

wear and tear

teddy bear

unbearable humidity

to wear out

great grandchild

great grandmother

to break the ice

to wear away

a big bear hug

Underline and re-read the phrases that name things that can be manufactured.

cry	carry	drowsy
crying	carried	drowsily
crier	carrier	drowsier
cried	carrying	drowsiness

hurry	pray	mighty
hurried	prayer	mightiest
hurriedly	praying	mightier
hurrying	prayed	mightily

storm	empty	shaky
stormy	emptier	shakiness
stormier	emptied	shakiest
stormiest	emptiness	shakily
storminess	emptying	shakier

lazy	pay	happy
lazily	payment	happily
laziness	payer	happier
lazier	paying	happiness
laziest	payless	happiest

play	copy	gray
playful	copied	grayness
player	copying	grayish
playing	copier	grayer

earn	earnings	earthquake
heard	early	searchlight
learn	rehearse	earliest
pearl	research	unearthed
yearn	rehearsal	learned
earth	earthworm	searches
search	overheard	earlier

Earth Day	search engine
down to earth	earned her respect
bright and early	heard a rumor
yearned for success	an early dinner
the planet Earth	in search of
a research paper	pearly white teeth
early in the morning	unheard of
a pearl necklace	dress rehearsal
learned to dance	the earlier the better
Web search	to earn a living

Underline and re-read the phrases that tell *when*.

The Earth

1. Earth is a planet spinning in space.

2. Earth is the fifth largest planet and the third planet from the sun.

3. Mercury, Venus, Earth, and Mars are nearest the sun and are called the inner planets.

4. Earth depends on the sun for light and heat.

5. It takes Earth one year to orbit around the sun.

6. The core, or center, of the earth is about one hundred times hotter than the hottest desert.

7. The mantle of the earth is just below the crust and goes down to the core.

8. It takes Earth one day to rotate one complete turn on its axis.

9. The sudden shift of the earth's crust can cause an earthquake.

10. A volcano is an opening in Earth's crust from which molten rock, or lava, is sometimes forced out.

11. Three quarters of the earth is covered by water.

12. The South Pole is the coldest place on Earth.

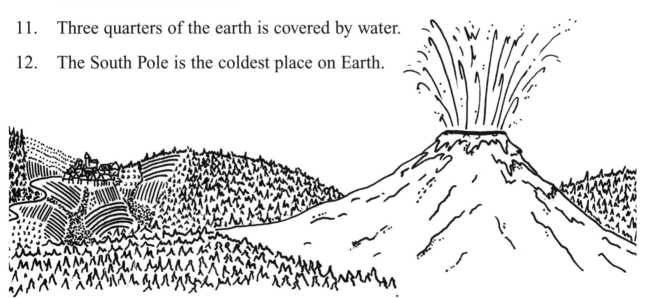

Underline and re-read the sentences that tell about the movement of the Earth.

dear	steak	already
pear	wear	beard
meat	spread	search
beat	seat	instead
heat	breath	yearn
streak	bear	early
break	heat	weak
earth	hear	ready
bread	seal	deafening
great	deaf	heading
head	lean	feather
swear	bead	breathe
sweat	health	heave
learn	heard	earrings
deal	heal	tearful
meant	spear	sweater
hear	meal	reading
earn	year	breakfast

Circle the words in which *ea* is pronounced ĕ.

vault	August	because
cause	author	exhaust
launch	saucer	applause
pause	faucet	haunted
sauce	sausage	automatic
haul	applaud	dinosaur
fault	faulty	astronaut
gauze	default	applesauce
haunt	laundry	exhausted

---

haunted house	leaky faucet
cup and saucer	always exhausted
dirty laundry	caused an earthquake
worthy causes	cause and effect
hot sauce	launched a satellite
a round of applause	to pause for a moment
a well-known author	eggs and sausage
a dinosaur egg	a brave astronaut
at fault	every August

Circle the words that name professions.

Silent *e*, Doubling, and *Y* Rules

Root Word	Suffix	Silent *e* Rule	Doubling Rule	*y* Rule	New Word
cute	-est	X			cutest
carry	-ed				
surprise	-ing				
plan	-ing				
stay	-ed				
run	-er				
steady	-ed				
exercise	-ing				
delay	-ed				
fog	-y				
early	-er				
cause	-ing				
ready	-ly				
buy	-ing				
drop	-ed				

Decide whether to apply the silent *e*, doubling, or *y* rule to add each suffix, and then put an X in the appropriate box.

Add each suffix to the root word, and read the new word.

law	claw	drawer
saw	straw	coleslaw
jaw	lawn	seesaw
raw	drawn	awning
paw	shawl	tomahawk
draw	yawn	unlawful
hawk	crawl	strawberry
dawn	lawyer	drawbridge
thaw	awful	drawing

---

mother-in-law	father-in-law
lawn mower	law and order
squawking parrots	strawberry ice cream
drawn shades	the last straw
to enforce the law	from dawn to dusk
to draw and paint	to thaw out
to mow the lawn	an awful mess

Circle phrases that name things a child can do.

1.	How many quarts are there in one gallon?	
2.	How old will you be in thirty years?	
3.	If you have a hundred pennies and you want to exchange them for quarters, how many quarters will you get?	
4.	How many inches are in two feet?	
5.	If I weigh eighty-two pounds and my little brother weighs fifty-three pounds, what is the difference in our weight?	
6.	What is the name of the shape that has three sides and three angles?	
7.	What do you call a rectangle with four equal sides?	
8.	If you add twelve, twenty-three, and forty-five together, what is the sum?	
9.	What is the product of 7 fives?	
10.	My grandmother asked me to buy her two dozen eggs. How many eggs are there in two dozen?	
11.	If there are sixteen ounces in one pound, how many ounces are there in three pounds?	
12.	If you were first in line and I was thirteenth in line, how many people would be between us?	

Answer the math questions.

food	broom	stoop
troop	spool	soon
swoop	loom	proof
zoo	bloom	roost
snooze	boom	pool
loop	mood	moose
noon	groom	cool
shoot	boot	boost
roof	zoom	root
hoop	drool	fool
spoon	gloom	tooth
too	scoop	room
stool	groove	moon
loose	droop	snoop
brood	booth	goose

In the first column, circle a synonym for *also*.
In the second column, circle a synonym for *sag*.
In the third column, circle a synonym for *spy*.

toothbrush	toothpaste	caboose
balloon	papoose	shampoo
cartoon	scooter	noodle
igloo	bathroom	raccoon
baboon	whirlpool	waterproof
harpoon	moonlight	foolish
carpool	moody	rooster
poodle	teaspoon	afternoon
mushroom	bedroom	classroom
ovenproof	doodle	tattoo
seafood	moonlight	proofread
tablespoon	kangaroo	fireproof

Circle words that name kinds of illustrations.

bride and groom	a loose tooth
need some proof	French poodle
ice cream scoop	goose down quilt
a diving pool	flowers in bloom
a spool of thread	moose antlers
playing hoops	three-legged stool
hiking boots	shoot the breeze
health food	an electric broom
snooped around	woven on a loom
waterproof boots	in a great mood
sooner or later	as cool as a cucumber
to throw a boomerang	a motor scooter
as smooth as glass	eighth grade classroom
a funny cartoon	snowy rooftops
a drooling baby	a ray of moonlight
wild mushrooms	hot air balloon
a family of raccoons	emergency room
one teaspoonful	acting foolishly
a toothbrush holder	ovenproof baking dish

Underline the simile in each column, and use it in a sentence.

When adding the suffix *s to words ending in y...*

If there a **consonant** before the *y*, change the *y* to *i* and add *-es*.

If there is **vowel** before the *y*, just add an *s*.

Root Word	Consonant	Vowel	New Word
lady	X		ladies
ray		X	rays
candy			
fly			
party			
day			
buy			
story			
delay			
stay			
berry			
try			
penny			
play			

Put an X in the box to show the kind of letter that comes before the Y. Add the suffix and read the new word.

city	cities		baby	
couch			birthday	
church			hobby	
paw			story	
sandwich			party	
cherry			family	
cry			discovery	
bread			address	

1. Some of the men on the basketball team were over seven feet tall.

2. There were many deer in the woods.

3. The gaggle of geese was making a racket.

4. Sheep grazed in the meadow.

5. Did you invite eighteen children to your party?

6. If we get four women together, we can play bridge.

7. Mice love to eat cheese.

8. By the time he was eleven months old, the baby had a mouth full of teeth.

Write the plural form of each word.
Underline the irregular plurals in the sentences.

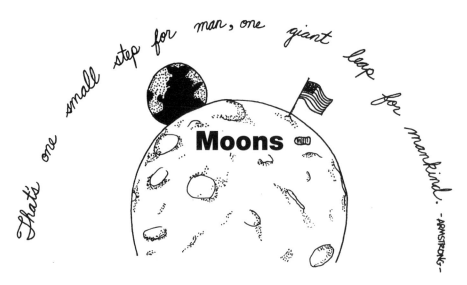

Moons

1. The moon is about one quarter the size of Earth.

2. The moon orbits around the earth about once every twenty-eight days.

3. We can only see one side of the moon from Earth.

4. When the side of the moon facing Earth is fully lit by the sun, we see a full moon.

5. The moon does not make its own light but reflects the light from the sun.

6. The moon is the second brightest object in the sky, after the sun.

7. On July 20, 1969, the astronaut Neil Armstrong was the first human being to walk on the moon.

8. Neil Armstrong's footprints will remain on the moon for many years because there is no wind on the moon.

9. There is no air on the moon, but ice has been discovered on its poles.

10. A solar eclipse occurs when the moon is between the sun and the Earth, and its shadow moves across the face of the Earth.

11. Some planets have more than one moon, and some planets have none.

12. Jupiter has over sixteen known moons and may have more than twenty-eight!

book	woolen	barefoot
good	woodwind	fishhook
look	wooden	bookshelf
took	redwood	textbook
foot	notebook	wooden
wood	football	goodness
hook	cookbook	scrapbook
stood	understood	childhood
hood	bookends	firewood
shook	lookout	footsteps
brook	footprint	woodpecker
crook	footnote	footwear
cook	bookmark	neighborhood
wool	pocketbook	misunderstood

Circle the words that name things you might find in a forest.

finally understood	good-looking
redwood forests	hooded sweatshirt
woolen sweater	ran barefoot
football helmet	a babbling brook
a wooden bookshelf	good advice
writer's notebook	a math textbook
booked a flight	to knock on wood
a Chinese cookbook	shook hands
reference books	in good health
the foot of the bed	a book of matches
built-in bookcases	to hit the books
a woolly mammoth	good-natured
woodwind instruments	a crooked branch
an attendance book	childhood friends

Underline and re-read phrases that name things you might find in a library.

half

1. If you have half of something, you have one of two equal parts.

2. Even numbers can always be split in half.

3. My watch says it is half past eleven.

4. Half of one thousand is five hundred.

5. The bookshelf was on sale for half price.

6. I was halfway to school when I remembered I was going to have a test today in math.

7. I'll do my homework when it's half time in the football game.

8. Is the glass half empty or half full?

9. If a ton equals two thousand pounds, how many pounds are there in half a ton?

10. If there are four quarts in a gallon, how many quarts are there in half a gallon?

11. How many inches are there in half a foot?

12. What is half of one dozen?

Answer the questions in the last four sentences.

lie	tie	die
lied	tied	died
lying	tying	dying

piece	shriek	infield
chief	thieves	outfield
field	cookie	cashier
niece	frontier	relieved
brief	relief	mouthpiece
pier	achieve	battlefield
shield	belief	masterpiece
priest	believe	windshield
thief	diesel	achievement
fierce	briefly	unbelievable

ceiling	conceive	weird
receive	perceive	either
deceive	conceited	neither

Circle the words that refer to different kinds of people

oatmeal cookie	cookie cutter
as easy as pie	make-believe
shirt and tie	right fielder
a white lie	a piece of wood
untied his boots	pie chart
the fierce tiger	lie down
Boston cream pie	piece of cake
commander in chief	field of wheat
a brief speech	a frightening shriek
a fierce argument	common belief
a diesel truck	relief map
broken windshield	an unbelievable masterpiece
supermarket clerk	eight foot high ceilings
received advice	either one or the other
neither one	the brave chief
piece by piece	her greatest achievement
trumpet's mouthpiece	hit the ceiling
football fields	to catch a thief

Underline and re-read the phrases that might answer the question *Who?*

Why did the grizzly buy a pair of boots?
He had bear feet.

How do rabbits keep their fur in place?
They use hare spray.

What did the chicken hit in the baseball game?
He hit a fowl ball.

How do you know that horses don't like oats?
They always say neigh to them.

What kind of insect is the best outfielder?
A spider is the best outfielder because it always catches **flies**.

Why isn't a dog's nose twelve inches long?
If it were twelve inches long, it would be a **foot**.

When is a piece of wood like a king?
It is like a king when it is a **ruler**.

What did one candle say to the other?
Are you **going out** tonight?

Find the homonyms in the answers to the first four riddles.
Discuss the multiple meanings of the words in bold in the last four riddles.

join	joint	avoid
noise	voice	turquoise
choice	coin	embroider
soil	moist	disappoint
oil	broil	unavoidable
coil	broiler	disappointed
boil	moisten	appointment
spoil	poison	embroidery

---

joined together	shining turquoise seas
broiled sirloin steak	poison mushrooms
a murmur of voices	motor oil
to confirm an appointment	a gruff voice
point-and-click	boiling water
to burn the midnight oil	an embroidered shirt
poison ivy	joined the crowd
too much noise	a difficult choice
to spoil the surprise	oil fields
turning point	to toss a coin

Underline and re-read the phrases that name things you might want to avoid.

toy	boyish	destroy
boy	voyage	employ
soy	boyhood	employer
joy	joyful	enjoyable
tomboy	soybean	enjoyment
enjoy	oyster	unenjoyable
annoy	cowboy	corduroy

---

raw oysters	exciting voyage
boyish grin	an annoying habit
an enjoyable day	boyhood dreams
an oyster shell	soy sauce
pride and joy	maiden voyage
full of joy	boys and girls
an annoying itch	soy beans
a boy's voice	the joy of cooking
corduroy pants	a kindly employer

Underline the noun or nouns in each phrase.

Root Word	Suffix	New Word
dirty	-ed	
easy	-ly	
play	-er	
annoy	-ing	
buy	-ing	
employ	-ed	
cloudy	-er	
enjoy	-able	
lucky	-ly	
boy	-ish	
moody	-ness	
heavy	-er	
sloppy	-est	
destroy	-er	
hurry	-ed	
destroy	-ing	
oily	-ness	
annoy	-ed	

Add each suffix to the root word, and read the new word.

caught　　**daughter**　　**taught**

1. That mother and daughter look exactly alike.

2. Having to stay after school to finish my homework really taught me a lesson.

3. After running all the way across town, I finally caught up with my friends.

4. My niece went to Africa last August and taught children to speak English.

5. I caught a cold and missed one week of school last month.

6. My father taught me how to swim when I was four years old.

7. After I caught a big fish, I tossed it back into the river.

8. My mother taught me to treat people kindly.

9. Her granddaughter is a well-known lawyer.

10. After a few seconds, everyone caught on to the joke.

11. My homeroom teacher has two daughters and a son.

12. I caught a glimpse of the parade as it went by.

Underline and re-read the sentences in which *caught* means *got*.

rough   **tough**   **enough**

1. When I kiss my grandfather, his beard feels rough as sandpaper.

2. Firefighters have a tough job.

3. The sea voyage was unpleasant because of the rough waters.

4. My daughter did not get a perfect score on her math test, but she did well enough.

5. This one child makes enough noise for two children!

6. It's great to have a pick-up truck when driving on rough roads.

7. We didn't enjoy dinner last night because the sirloin steaks were so tough.

8. Last year was a tough winter, with over ten major snowstorms.

9. I know how to cook well enough to make simple dishes.

10. I printed out a rough draft of my book report so I could work on revising it.

11. Are there enough oatmeal cookies for everyone?

12. Are corduroy pants good enough to wear to your daughter's birthday party?

Underline and re-read the sentences that happened in the past.

blue	argue	bluebird
glue	value	overdue
clue	rescue	continue
due	pursue	avenue
sue	tissue	Tuesday
fuel	issue	barbeque
true	statue	blueberries

---

blue whales	continues on Tuesday
blue jeans	due date
tissue paper	barbequed steak
overdue books	blueberry pancakes
fuel oil	pursued the thief
past due	a daring rescue
a glue stick	Statue of Liberty
to argue against	searching for clues
barbeque sauce	a true-blue friend
place value	feeling blue
a back issue	once in a blue moon
a hot issue	out of the blue

102 Discuss the figurative meaning of the last four idioms in the second column.

The Days of the Week

1. The day before Wednesday is _____ .

2. Thanksgiving always falls on a _____ .

3. The day named after the moon is _____ .

4. The day before Thursday is _____ .

5. The last day of the week is _____ .

6. The day after tomorrow is _____ .

7. The day before yesterday was _____ .

8. The middle day of the week is _____ .

Write the days of the week in order.

guess	guilt	guitar
guy	guard	guilty
guest	disguise	guidance
guide	lifeguard	guestroom

---

guard dog	caught off guard
guessing game	not guilty
thirty dinner guests	the Coast Guard
to guard against injury	guide word
a guilty look	guessed right
a wild guess	an electric guitar
a great guy	to be on guard
to feel guilty	slept in the guestroom
to guess again	a clever disguise
rescued by the lifeguard	guidance counselor
checked the guidebooks	guessed my age

motion	location	subtraction
nation	dictation	injection
lotion	exploration	selection
station	imagination	prediction
vacation	constellation	traction
pollution	addition	friction
celebration	definition	collection
donation	tradition	construction
emotion	conditon	direction
conversation	edition	fraction
education	position	affection
communication	composition	caption
operation	action	digestion
transportation	connection	disruption
population	election	mention
rotation	fiction	adoption
revolution	protection	multiplication
infection	consideration	attention

Circle the math words.

a constellation of stars

used her imagination

air-conditioned

multiplication tables

caught my attention

a nonfiction story

to make a donation

to take a position

good for digestion

missed my connection

comparing fractions

the election of a president

a paperback edition

railroad station

an exciting conversation

to take public transportation

a cartoon caption

coin collection

a soothing lotion

United Nations

water pollution

public education

a well-written composition

a long-standing tradition

a birthday celebration

the rotation of Earth

to go on a family vacation

full of affection

addition and subtraction

to cause a disruption

to make a prediction

to point in the right direction

Underline and re-read the phrases that name things you might study in social studies.

affect

affected

affection

subtract

subtracting

subtracted

subtraction

protect

protects

protected

protection

unprotected

prevent

preventing

prevented

preventable

prevention

explore

explorer

explored

exploring

exploration

add

added

adding

addition

additional

nation

national

international

define

defined

defining

definition

consider

considered

considering

considerable

consideration

pollute

polluter

polluting

polluted

pollution

educate

educated

educating

educator

education

edit

editing

editor

edited

edition

silent b	silent h	silent t
lamb	hour	often
numb	herb	listen
dumb	heir	fasten
limb	heirloom	soften
thumb	honest	glisten
crumb	honor	whistle
comb	ghost	castle
climb	exhibit	wrestle
plumber	herbal	rustle
dumbbell	rhinoceros	bristle
thumbnail	honesty	gristle
thumbtack	rhombus	thistle
	hourglass	
	honestly	
	honorable	

an honest mistake	toothbrush bristles
apple crumb cake	cold and numb
Honest Abe	lower limbs
as meek as a lamb	a comb and brush
a charging rhinoceros	rock climbing
all thumbs	rush hour
clean as a whistle	herb garden
climbing the walls	on the hour
a green thumb	to arm wrestle
out on a limb	listening to ghost stories
white rhinoceros	a tree limb
a tough wrestling match	the rustling leaves
taught me to whistle	to fasten your seat belts
an exhibit of heirlooms	strikes every hour
eight pound dumbbells	guarding the castle
softened by lotion	often take vacations
very tough gristle	honor guard
guest of honor	glistening in the sun

Underline the idioms in the first column, and then discuss their literal and figurative meaning.

new	grew	curfew
flew	crew	jewelry
news	few	newborn
dew	blew	renew
knew	pew	newscast
chew	newest	jeweler
drew	sewer	newspaper
stew	jewel	screwdriver
brew	cashew	New York
threw	mildew	New Zealand
screw	pewter	New England

Circle the words that are past-tense verbs.

early-morning dew	newspaper reporter
lamb stew	threw out
an early curfew	as fresh as dew
news conference	to break the news
a cashew tree	front-page news
headline news	brand-new edition
New Year's Eve	quite a few
the new moon	chewed up
church pew	drew a circle
costume jewelry	threw away
to brew a pot of coffee	grew up
crew cut	drew near
grew cotton	oyster stew
only a few donations	drew a deep breath
grew cold	to bite off more than one can chew
flew away	threw cold water on my plans

Discuss the literal and figurative meanings of the last three idioms in the second column.

you	wounded	juicy
youth	youthful	lawsuit
soup	juice	suitcase
group	suit	grapefruit
wound	fruit	nuisance
soupy	cruise	suitable
coupon	bruise	unsuitable

---

grapefruit juice	fruit salad
bathing suit	tomato juice
vegetable soup	sweat suit
in her youth	such a nuisance
a group of buildings	wounded feelings
soup kitchen	youthful energy
fruit bowl	a juicy grapefruit
a group of children	to collect coupons
huge cruise ships	a suitable education

Underline and re-read phrases that refer to liquids.

Silent *e*, Doubling, and *Y* Rules

Root Word	Suffix	Silent *e* Rule	Doubling Rule	*Y* Rule	No Change	New Word
juicy	-est			X		juciest
settle	-ment					
healthy	-ly					
hour	-ly					
guide	-ed					
relay	-ed					
whistle	-ed					
lovely	-est					
pause	-ed					
choice	-est					
juice	-y					
climb	-er					
red	-ish					
listen	-ed					
wrestle	-er					

Decide whether or not to apply the silent *e*, doubling, or *y* rule to add each suffix, and then put an X in the appropriate box.

Add each suffix to the root word, and read the new word.

i/o	e/o	i/a	u/a
lion	neon	giant	truant
lioness	video	diary	truancy
pioneer	cameo	dial	January
riot	rodeo	trial	February
iodine	peony	triangle	evaluate
Ohio	peonies	reliable	evaluation
Iowa	meteor	defiant	evacute
violin	meteorite	defiance	evacuation
violinist	meteorology	diagnose	graduate
violet	meteorologist	diagonal	graduation
violent	geology		situation
violate	geologist		
violence	geometry		
violation	geometric		
biology	deodorant		
biologist			

neon lights	a video camera
a meteor shower	violet peonies
learned geology	studied geometry
a right triangle	a giant lioness
diagonal stripes	the truant officer
graduation ceremony	a traveling rodeo
parking violation	the violin section
diagnosed the disease	attended biology class
a jury trial	kept a diary
a bottle of iodine	to violate the rules
the violence of the storm	the lion's share
played video games	the concert violinist
a pride of lions	a violent thunderstorm
geometric patterns	graduated high school
a defiant manner	to evacuate a building
reliable information	a pioneer in space exploration

Underline and re-read the phrases that describe what a high school student might have done.   115

The Months of the Year

1. How many months are in a year? _____

2. My brother's birthday is two months from today. When is it? _____

3. What month comes after July? _____

4. In which month does Columbus Day fall? _____

5. Three months ago was _____ .

6. Thanksgiving is the fourth Thursday in _____ .

7. The month before February is _____ .

8. New Year's Eve is the last day in _____ .

9. In which month does Washington's birthday fall? _____ .

10. If today was your thirteenth birthday, when would you be 13½?

    _____?

11. Name the months with 31 days. _____,

_____, _____, _____,

_____, _____, _____ .

Thirty days have September,
April, June, and November.
All the rest have thirty-one,
Except February alone,
Which has twenty-eight days, rain or shine,
And each leap year, twenty-nine.

mansion	percussion	possession
passion	discussion	permission
session	admission	expression
tension	expansion	intermission
mission	impression	suppression
submission	extension	omission
confession	suspension	compassion
transmission	passionate	comprehension

recording session	high tension wire
the tension of the bow	passion fruit
rescue mission	a passion for music
permission slip	percussion instruments
suspension bridge	reading with expression
discussion group	westward expansion
a half-hour intermission	valuable possessions
to make a good impression	extension cord
a full confession	the price of admission
reading comprehension	beyond my comprehension

Underline and re-read the phrase in each column that names something you might need for a class trip.   117

vision	division	decision
version	conclusion	confusion
collision	transfusion	explosion
invasion	erosion	precision
exclusion	revision	occasion
excursion	television	supervision

---

to draw a conclusion	avoided a collision
long division	short version
a difficult decision	in conclusion
television stations	blood transfusion
a giant explosion	tunnel vision
the final revision	an important occasion
took a weekend excursion	careful supervision
invasion of ants	to do on occasion
to the exclusion of all else	an important decision
cut with precision	land erosion

conclude
concludes
concluded
conclusion

decide
decides
decided
decision
indecision

collide
colliding
collides
collided
collision

confuse
confuses
confused
confusing
confusion

extend
extended
extends
extending
extension

erode
erodes
eroding
eroded
erosion

admit
admitting
admitted
admission

permit
permits
permitting
permitted
permission

impress
impresses
impressive
impressed
impression

divide
divided
dividing
divides
division

revise
revises
revising
revised
revision

discuss
discussed
discusses
discussing
discussion

certain	uncertain
mountain	fountain
captain	bargain
villain	certainly
curtain	mountainside

---

mountain climbing	Great Britain
mountain lion	captain of the football team
a mountain of homework	heavy curtains
volcanic mountain	a fountain pen
absolutely certain	to drive a hard bargain
to draw the curtains	to be certain about
still uncertain	bargain prices
a water fountain	played the villain
cruise ship captain	fearless mountaineer

Underline the phrases that are idioms, and discuss their literal and figurative meanings.

Mountains

1. A mountain is a high hill with a steep slope.

2. A chain of mountains is called a range.

3. Mountain ranges are found on every continent in the world.

4. One of the longest mountain ranges in the world is found in the western United States.

5. The Rocky Mountains extend from northern Canada to New Mexico.

6. The tallest mountain in the world, Mt. Everest, is 29,035 feet above sea level.

7. Mountains grow, change their shape, and wear away.

8. Mountains are eroded, or worn down, by wind, rain and ice.

9. Animals such as mountain lions and goats live high on mountaintops, where the air becomes very cold.

10. Some mountains are so cold that they are covered with snow all year.

11. There are even mountains on the moon!

12. A gorge is a deep, narrow passage between two mountains.

Underline in the sentences any phrases that tell where mountains are found.

nature	lecture	adventure
feature	pasture	signature
picture	capture	furniture
feature	gesture	overture
fracture	fixture	departure
creature	texture	temperature
mixture	posture	literature
culture	structure	manufacture
vulture	sculpture	agriculture
puncture	moisture	legislature

Circle words that name things you can buy.

nature trails	the broken light fixture
furniture polish	a hasty departure
elbow fracture	an overture to an opera
excellent posture	below freezing temperatures
needs your signature	to study Native American culture
punctured tire	a risky adventure
to plan for the future	children's literature
a strange mixture	moisture in the air
captured the vulture	manufactured computers
human nature	a frightening creature
in the near future	a ruptured appendix
a promising future	a motion picture
green pastures	her daughter's picture
state legislature	his best feature
drawing a picture	good natured

Underline and re-read the phrases that name things that need to be repaired.

FOOTBALL
ANGLERFISH

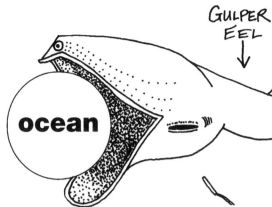

GULPER
EEL

ocean

1. Oceans are large bodies of salt water that cover most of the Earth.

2. All five oceans flow into one another to make a gigantic world ocean.

3. The Pacific Ocean is larger than all the other oceans.

4. The tallest mountains on Earth are found underwater in the oceans.

5. The moon's gravity pulls the water in the Earth's oceans toward it, causing tides.

6. In most parts of the world, ocean water rises and falls twice a day in tides.

7. No light reaches the bottom of the deepest ocean depths, and yet strange-looking fish manage to live there.

8. People need to protect the oceans from pollution.

← HATCHET
FISH

9. Over 13,000 kinds of fish live in the oceans.

10. The oceans have great bands of water, called currents, that flow like rivers.

11. All rivers to the east of the Rocky Mountains flow to the Atlantic Ocean.

12. The Arctic Ocean is the smallest of the five world oceans, and parts of it are always covered with ice.

WONDER FISH

Underline and re-read the sentences that tell about the movement of oceans.

island

1. An island is a piece of land completely surrounded by water.

2. An oceanic island is an island in the sea, far from any continent.

3. Huge floating islands of ice can be found in the Arctic Ocean.

4. Some mountain peaks rise out of oceans to form islands.

5. Some islands are found in rivers and lakes, but most are found in oceans.

6. Animals and plants that live on islands are often different from those found in other places.

7. Great Britain is a large island that includes England, Scotland, and Wales.

8. Ellis Island, a small island in New York Harbor, was once the chief immigration station of the United States.

9. Many islands around the world have been formed by volcanoes.

10. In 1886, the Statue of Liberty was assembled on Liberty Island in New York Harbor.

Underline and re-read the sentences that tell different ways islands can be made.

phone	phantom	biography
graph	dolphin	pharmacy
photo	elephant	geography
phase	telephone	alphabetical
phrase	graphite	pharmacist
trophy	pheasant	photography
sphere	photograph	photographer
phonics	phoocopy	hemisphere
phony	autobiography	calligraphy
orphan	nephew	paragraph
gopher	alphabet	alphabetize
saxophone	headphones	atmosphere

Circle each word that names a kind of book.

cell phone

Western Hemisphere

an African elephant

compared the bar graphs

practiced reading phrases

phases of the moon

swimming with dolphins

adopted two orphans

a football trophy

the gopher's burrow

telephone number

a pleasant atmosphere

a bar graph

elegant calligraphy

a descriptive paragraph

niece and nephew

photo finish

took photographs

a photography show

the cursive alphabet

a solid wooden sphere

an exhibit of black and white photos

a phony gold bracelet

the neighborhood pharmacy

frightened by the phantom

long-distance phone calls

the pheasant's long tail

the atmosphere on Mars

a photography contest

alphabetical order

digital photography

a phase of life

a well-written paragraph

studied oceanography

Underline and re-read the phrases that name things that can be written.

- phone is a Greek root that means *sound*	**- graph** is a Greek root that means *write*

phonics	graphics	geography
telephone	graphite	biography
megaphone	telegraph	cartography
saxophone	photograph	calligraphy
headphone	paragraph	photography
	autograph	autobiography

1. Graphite is used to make lead pencils because it is nontoxic.

2. Alexander Graham Bell invented the telephone.

3. Before the telephone was invented, people sent messages by telegraph.

4. Cartography is the art of making maps.

5. We use phonics to read and spell.

6. A megaphone is a device shaped like a cone that is used to make the sound of the voice louder.

7. Many years before there were computers, people used pen and ink to produce beautiful calligraphy.

8. An autobiography is a story of a person's life written by that person.

9. The autographs of some well-known people are worth a lot.

10. Digital photography allows you to alter photos on your computer and print them out!

The End